CW00393816

Unleashed SONGBOOK

60 SONGS FOR THE CHURCH
WITH FULL SCORES

COPYRIGHT & PHOTOCOPYING

ACKNOWLEDGEMENTS

Music arranging/setting: David Ball | davidoxon@aol.com
Artwork: CPO | cpo.org.uk
Executive Producer: Peter Martin

Special thanks to Brenda Cameron and all at Cambron Software for Power Music and your help in developing this resource.

Spring Harvest wishes to acknowledge and thank the following people for their help in the compilation and production of this songbook: Denise Anstead, Pete Broadbent, Andrew Crookall, Rachel Gray, Cheryl Jenkinson & Sue Rinaldi.

Published & distributed by Essential Christian, 14 Horsted Square, Uckfield, East Sussex, TN22 1QG, UK. An activity of Memralife Group, Registered Charity number 1126997, a Company limited by guarantee, registered in England and Wales, number 6667924. Registered Office: 14 Horsted Square, Uckfield, East Sussex, TN22 1QG.

ISBN 978-1-911237-15-0

CONTENTS

DISCOVER THE SPRING HARVEST DIGITAL SONGBOOK

Over the years of the Spring Harvest Songbook, we have always been looking at how we can use technology to make worship leaders' lives easier and make the flow of worship smoother. Power Music has been at the heart of our digital songbooks since 2011 and is widely used by worship musicians to free themselves from the hassles of paper music. In Power Music all your music is instantly available on-screen for practice and performance.

Once again we have worked in partnership with Power Music to create a digital version of the Spring Harvest 2020 Songbook. This includes sheet music, chord sheets, lyrics and all the indexing required to find your songs quickly.

Use your iPad, PC, laptop, Windows tablet or Mac as a "digital" music stand to display music or chord sheets on-screen.

WHY USE POWER MUSIC?

 Songs are easy to find by title, first line, category, author and Bible reference

 Quickly set up playlists for your services

 Transpose chord sheets, add capo chords

 Add performance notes

 Link audio tracks for practice or performance.

 Using multiple screens keeps the whole band on the same page

 Synchronised iPad display

 Page turning becomes simple using a foot pedal or by simply tapping a screen or a keyboard.

No more searching for scraps of paper, no more filing song sheets, no more photocopying - Power Music makes worship times stress free for musicians.

iPAD

Get Spring Harvest 2020 Songbook on your iPad using the free Power Music app.

DOWNLOAD* (Windows & mac OS X)

- Display sheet music and chord sheets
- Transpose chord sheets
- Search by title, author, category, Bible reference

Find your unique reference code on the inside front cover

 Windows

Mac

HELP*

Getting started

*See inside front cover for details

ALPHABETICAL INDEX

[Song titles differing from first lines are in italics]

essential
christian
presents

SPRING
HARVEST
2020

Unleashed

SONGBOOK

ALWAYS TRUE, ALWAYS KIND
(THIS IS THE DAY)

Key = B

CCLI# 7133418

AMAZING LOVE! HOW CAN IT BE
(I FALL DOWN ON MY KNEES)

Key = D

Colin Webster & Ben Slee

Verse

♩ = 70

| D | | | | | G | |

1. A - maz - ing love! How can it be that you my
2. No trace of good you found in me, that you should
3. O bro - ken Lamb, what love is this that held you
4. Oh Je - sus where could I be - gin to count the

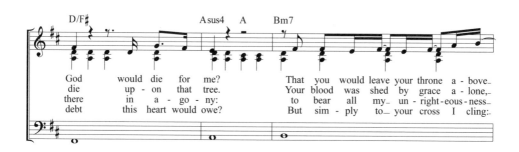

| D/F♯ | | | A sus4 | A | Bm7 |

God would die for me? That you would leave your throne a - bove
die up - on that tree. Your blood was shed by grace a - lone,
there in a - go - ny: to bear all my un - right-eous-ness
debt this heart would owe? But sim - ply to your cross I cling:

| G | | D/F♯ | A sus4 | A | D |

(No repeat after v.3)

— to bleed for us — a - maz - ing love.
— by mer - cy deep, by love un - known.
— and pay the price to set me free?
— I give my heart, my life, my all.

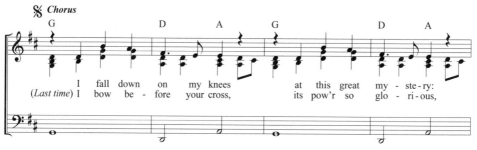

𝄋 Chorus

| G | | D | A | G | | D | A |

I fall down on my knees at this great my - ste - ry:
(Last time) I bow be - fore your cross, its pow'r so glo - ri - ous,

CCLI# 7141526

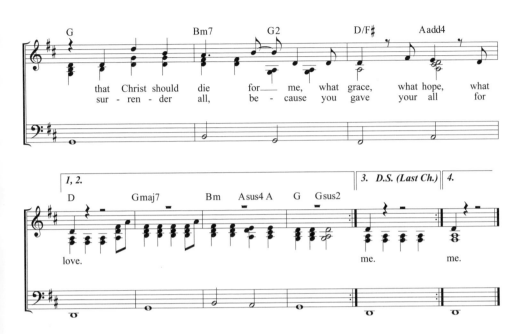

that Christ should die for___ me, what grace, what hope, what
sur - ren - der all, be - cause you gave your all for

love.   me.   me.

1, 2.

3. D.S. (Last Ch.) 4.

If you need help to find a song on a particular theme or Scripture passage, or just want to know which of the Spring Harvest songbooks or albums features the song you're after - use our song search.

» search online at **www.springharvest.org/resources/song-search/**

ARE YOU HURTING AND BROKEN WITHIN?

(O COME TO THE ALTAR)

Key = B

Christel.

Christ. O come to   Christ.   Oh, what a

Sa - viour,   is - n't he won - der - ful, sing al - le - lu - ia   Christ is ri - sen.____
fore him,   for he is Lord of   all, sing al - le - lu - ia   Christ is ri - sen.____

Bow down be   O come to
Oh, what a

Christ.____

ARISE MY SOUL
(SEE THE LIGHT)

Key = A

Ben Fielding & Reuben Morgan

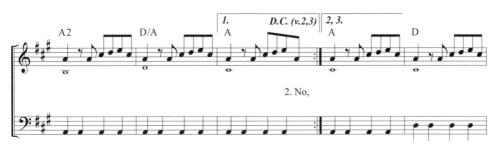

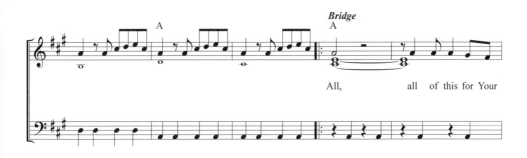

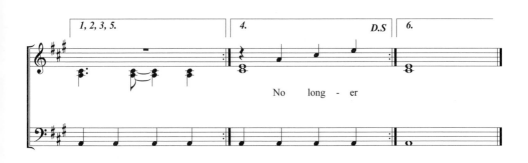

COME AND SEE
THE KING

Key = G

(YOU ARE THE CHRIST)

Olly Knight & Tom James

CCLI# 7112230

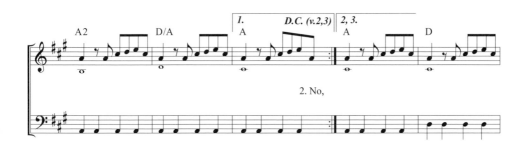

2. No,

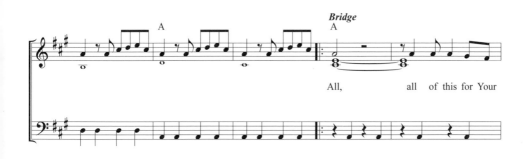

All,   all of this for Your

glo - ry.   All,   all of this for Your glo - ry.

No   long - er

COME HOLY SPIRIT, FILL US NOW
(COME HOLY SPIRIT)

Key = A

CCLI# 7137064

pass, and in your free-dom we'll see the chains fall off.__ We'll fol-low where you're

1. *D.C.* *2.* **Bridge**

mov-ing. mov-ing. Ig-nite our hearts, so faith and hope a-

rise, faith and hope a-rise. A-wake our pas-sion, let wor-ship be our

1. *2.* *D.C.* *Coda*

cry, let wor-ship be our cry. cry. __ Burn in us, we pray

Burn in us, we pray__

COME LET US WORSHIP OUR KING
(GREAT THINGS)

Key = A

Phil Wickham & Jonas Myrin

CCLI# 7111321

COME LIKE YOU WANT TO
(WELCOME THE HEALER)

Key = D

Brenton Brown, Brett Younker, Jess Cates,
Jourdan Johnson & Sean Curran

CCLI# 7123195

Dm7   F2   C

— We wel-come the Au - thor of — our faith.— We wel-come the God — who makes a way,

Last time to Coda ⊕ | 1. | 1° D.C.(v.3) | 3.   D.S
      2° D.S.S.

Dm7   F2   F2

— his name is — Je - sus, his name is — Je - sus.   sus.— We wel-come the Heal-

2.
F2   C5   Bridge (8va + rhythm on repeats)   C   Csus4   C   F2

- sus.—(oh)   Let   Your   liv - ing wa - ters   fall   on
           Come   and   bring the break-through, we   sur -

Am7   F/A   Am7   1, 2, 3.   4.
                F2   F2

sons and daugh-ters, we   will   not re-sist your— heart.   — God.
ren - der   to   you,   all   our   hope is in you,— God.

D.S   ⊕ Coda
        F2   C

We wel-come the Heal -   - sus.—

DID YOU KNOW, DID YOU KNOW
(GLOW)

Key = Dm

Capo 3 (Bm)

Sam Blake, Ian Yates & Hilary Sanders

♩ = 126

Verse

1. Did you know, did you know (what?) oh, oh, oh, oh (Yo!) The Ho-ly Spi-rit is our God liv-ing in-side us. Did you know, did you know (what?) oh, oh, oh, oh (Yo!)
2. Did you know, did you know (what?) oh, oh, oh, oh (Yo!) The Ho-ly Spi-rit is a- live and al-ways with us. Did you know, did you know (what?) oh, oh, oh, oh (Yo!)

We are the church and we're shin-ing in the dark-ness. Ho-ly Spi-rit
We are the church, light-ing up the world for Je-sus.

help us— to share— God's love, God's love. Po-wer to

glow, glow, glow._____ Po-wer to glow, glow, glow._____ By the

CCLI# 7145829

Ho-ly Spi-rit we are all em-po-wered to glow,___ to glow.___

Bridge

— Po-wer to —

Rap:
Thoughout all history, now no more mystery
The same Spirit lives in me, Holy… (GLOW), Holy… (GLOW)
Get up and glow, from our head to our toes
Pass on the glow, don't go with the flow
Glow on and on, glow in the dark
On your marks, get set… glow!

Glow - o - o___ — Po-wer to

Coda

ETERNAL FATHER, GRACIOUS KING
(LORD, IN YOUR MERCY)

Key = C

Ben Slee, Phil Moore & Tim Chester

1. E-ter-nal Fa-ther, gra-cious King, we come to you in prayer;
2. We come to you in Je-sus' name, we plead his pre-cious blood;
3. We come be-cause the Spi-rit speaks, to calm our doubt and fear;

ac-cept the pleas your child-ren bring, en-fold us in your care.
We leave be-hind our guilt and shame, se-cure with-in your love.
puts 'Ab-ba, Fa-ther' on our lips, and calls us to draw near.

Chorus

Lord, in your mer-cy, hear our prayer; Lord, in your mer-cy, hear our prayer. To your

throne of grace we come, by your Spi-rit, through your Son: in your mer-cy hear our

prayer.   prayer.

CCLI# 7133132

essential christian

NEW SONGS TO RESOURCE THE CHURCH

The perfect companion to the Spring Harvest Songbook!

13 songs of devotion and worship from leading songwriters. This album is a wonderful resource for learning and introducing new songs to churches, worship teams, or just for personal devotions. **All songs are featured in the songbook.**

FILL MY LUNGS WITH THE WIND OF YOUR SPIRIT
(EVERY BREATH)

Key = C

Hannah Hobbs & Ben Tan

1. Fill my lungs with the wind of your Spi - rit; breath to breath I'm de-pen-dent on you.___ Faith-ful God, you are call-ing me clos- er.
2. Tame my fears as I lean on your Spi - rit; trust-ing all of my heart un-to you.___ Let your pas-sion burn like a fi - re in my soul.

Pre-Chorus
1. When morn-ing dawns___ and eve - ning fades, I need your grace.
2. When morn-ing dawns___ and eve - ning fades I'll seek your face.

Chorus
Let ev-'ry breath I breathe pour out in praise to-ward the King, Je-sus, for - e - ver true, my ev-'ry breath will wor-ship you. you. Let ev-'ry you.

FOR WHAT WE HAVE DONE AND LEFT UNDONE

(FOR WHAT WE HAVE DONE (LORD, IN YOUR MERCY))

Key = C

Matt Papa, Matt Boswell, Aaron Keyes & James Thiele

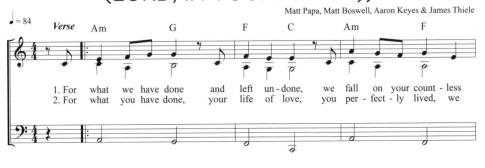

1. For what we have done and left un-done, we fall on your count-less
2. For what you have done, your life of love, you per-fect-ly lived, we

mer - cies.   For sins that are known and those un-known, we call on your name so
praise you.   Though temp-ted and tried, you fixed your eyes, you fin-ished the work God

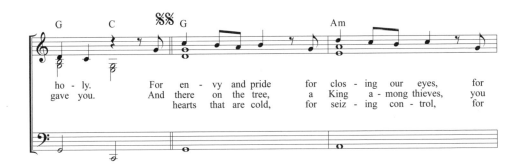

ho - ly.   For en - vy and pride   for clos - ing our eyes,   for
gave you.   And there on the tree,   a King a - mong thieves,   you
hearts that are cold,   for seiz - ing con - trol,   for

scorn - ing our ve - ry neigh-bour.   In thought word and deed   we've
bled for a world's be - tra - yal.   You loved to the end,   our
scorn - ing our ve - ry Ma - ker.   In thought word and deed,   we've

CCLI# 7136067

failed you our King, how deep - ly we need a Sa - viour.
mer - ci - ful friend, how pure and for - e - ver faith - ful.
failed you our King, how deep - ly we need a Sa - viour.

Chorus
F   G   C   G   F

Lord have me-rcy, Christ have mer-cy, Lord have mer-cy on___ us. Lord have mer-cy,

Last time to Coda
1.
G   Am   F   Gsus4 G   C   *D.C.*

Christ have mer - cy, Lord have mer - cy on_____ us.   2. For

2, 4, 5.   **3.**   *D.S.S. al Coda*
Am   G   Am   F   Gsus4 G   C

Lord have mer-cy on___ us. Lord have mer - cy on_____ us.   3. For

Coda
Am   F   Gsus4   G   C

Lord   have   mer - cy   on_____   us.

FROM LIFE'S BEGINNING
(LET PRAISE RESOUND)

Key = F

CCLI# 7126826

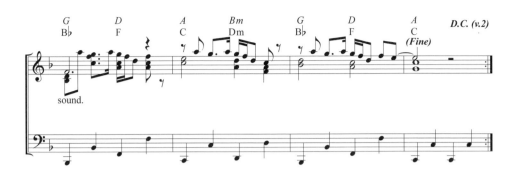

sound.

Bridge

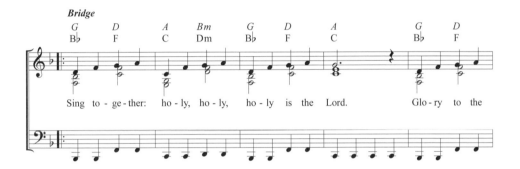

Sing to - ge - ther: ho - ly, ho - ly, ho - ly is the Lord. Glo - ry to the

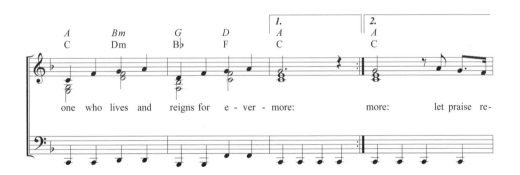

one who lives and reigns for e - ver - more: more: let praise re-

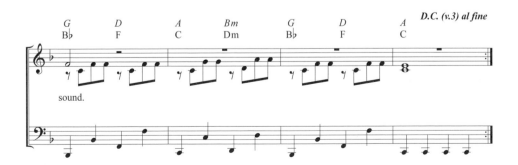

sound.

GOD, YOU BROUGHT US OUT OF THE WILDERNESS
(PRAISE UPON PRAISE)

Key = C

Ben Smith, Daniel Bashta,
Matt Redman & Pat Barrett

CCLI 7133378

the Lord. We sing praise— up-on praise, for grace— up-on grace, let

all that is with - in me praise— the Lord. We sing praise— up-on praise, for

grace— up-on grace, let all that is with-in me praise— the Lord. (We sing) 3. When my

Mid section

stand in awe of the ri - sen Son, O re-joice,— our song has just— be - gun. O re-joice,

— our song has just— be - gun. We sing

HE WHO WAS BEFORE THERE WAS LIGHT

(BEHOLD HIM)

Key = Eb

Paul Baloche & Mitch Wong

Capo 1 (D)

Verse

1. He who was be-fore there was light, walked a-
2. He who heard hu-ma-ni-ty's cry, left his
3. He who dined with sin-ners and saints, healed the
4. He who chose a cri-mi-nal's end, paid with

(Small notes v.4)

cross the pa-ges of time, He who made ev-'ry liv-ing thing, be-hold him.
throne to wake as a child, He be-came like the least of us, be-hold him.
blind, the lost and the lame, e-ven now he is in our midst, be-hold him.
blood to set-tle our debt, bu-ried death as he rose to life, be-hold him.

Chorus

1. Je - sus, Son of God, Mes - si - ah; the Lamb, the roar-ing Li - on,— oh,— be—
2. Je - sus, Al-pha and O - me - ga; our God, the Ri-sen Sa - viour, oh,— be—

Last time to Coda

D.C. (vv.3,4.)

still and be-hold him.
still and be

CCLI# 7133698

HERE IN THIS MOMENT
YOU ARE ABLE
(NO STORY YOU CAN'T REDEEM)

Key = G

Daniel Hill, David Walker, Micah Massey & Aaron Keyes

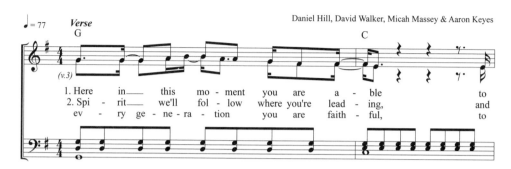

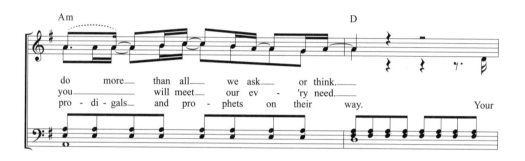

CCLI# 7123804

% G ... *Em* ... *C*

— to be - lieve_ for im - pos - si - ble things; we will not___ put our hope_ in a world_
-ture we dream for the heal - ing we need,_ if there's one___ thing we know: there's no sto -

1, 3, 5. D ... *2, 4, 6.* D sus4 ... G ... Em7

___ we can see._ For the fu - ry you can't_ re-deem.___

Last time to Coda ⊕ ... *1.* ... *D.C. (v.3)* ... *2.* ... *Bridge*
C ... Am ... Am ... G

3. To ... All things work to - ge -

1, 2, 3, 4, 5, 6, 7. ... *8.* ... *D.S.*
Em ... C ... D sus4 ... D sus4

- ther for our_ good,___ for our_ good.___ ___ We will choose___

⊕ *Coda*
Am ... G ... Em7 ... C ... Am ... G

essentialchristian.org

LIVE WORSHIP FROM SPRING HARVEST 2020

Order Now
Released
July 2020

ec
essential christian presents

SPRING HARVEST

Unleashed
LIVE WORSHIP

AARON KEYES & PETE JAMES
ELIM SOUND
LUCY GRIMBLE & KING'S VILLAGE
MOZAIEK WORSHIP WITH KEES KRAAYENOORD

Capturing the devotion and declaration of thousands of voices united in worship at Spring Harvest 2020, this album features Lead Worshippers **Aaron Keyes & Pete James**, **Elim Sound**, **Lucy Grimble & Kings Village**, and **Mozaiek Worship & Kees Kraayenoord**.

Available at essentialchristian.org/store, iTunes etc and Christian Bookshops

HOLY SPIRIT, GUIDE MY VISION
(HYMN OF THE HOLY SPIRIT)

Key = B♭

Jason Ingram, Chris Tomlin,
Brenton Brown & Pat Barrett

CCLI# 7113814

HOW GREAT THE CHASM THAT LAY BETWEEN US
(LIVING HOPE)

Key = D

Phil Wickham & Brian Johnson

CCLI# 7106807

Li - on de-clared 'the grave has no claim on me.' 3. Then came the

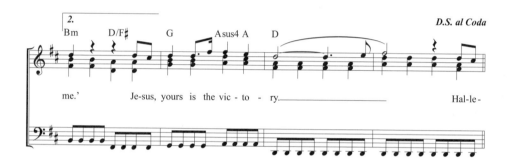

D.S. al Coda

me.' Je-sus, yours is the vic - to - ry._____ Hal-le-

Coda

hope. Je - sus Christ, my liv - ing hope. Oh God you

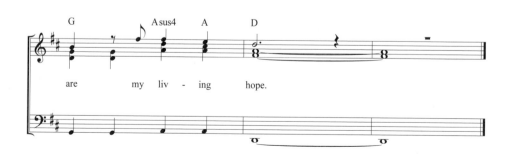

are my liv - ing hope.

 essential christian

essentialchristian.org

RECORDED TEACHING FROM
SPRING HARVEST

 SPRING HARVEST 2020

 Unleashed
THE **ACTS** CHURCH TODAY

Available on **CD, DVD***
and **USB stick**

*DVD of main meetings only

 SPRING HARVEST 2020 — Unleashed — THE **ACTS** CHURCH TODAY

Teaching DVD. Recorded live
essentialchristian.org/store

 ec Spring Harvest 2020

Teaching CD. Recorded live
essentialchristian.org/store

Make the teaching from Spring Harvest 2020 available to your church, home groups, friends and family. Share the messages from the 2020 theme of 'The Acts Church Today'. Practical, great theology, dynamic, thought provoking, and with the USBs containing every recorded talk, a great value library of teaching.

Over 46,000 recordings available from essentialchristian.org/store

I JUST WANT TO SPEAK THE NAME OF JESUS
(I SPEAK JESUS)

Key – C

Abby Benton, Carlene Prince, Dustin Smith,
Jesse Reeves, Kristen Dutton & Raina Pratt

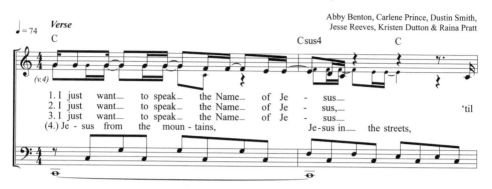

1. I just want to speak the Name of Je - sus
2. I just want to speak the Name of Je - sus, 'til
3. I just want to speak the Name of Je - sus
(4.) Je - sus from the moun - tains, Je - sus in the streets,

o - ver ev - 'ry heart and ev - 'ry mind. 'Cause
ev - 'ry dark ad - dic - tion starts to break. De -
o - ver fear and all an - xi - e - ty. To
Je - sus in the dark - ness o - ver ev - 'ry e - ne - my. Je -

1, 4, 5.

I know there is peace with - in your pre - sence, I speak Je - sus.
clar - ing there is hope and there is free - dom, I speak Je
ev - 'ry soul held cap - tive by de - pres - sion, I speak Je
- sus for my fam - 'ly, I speak the ho - ly Name, Je - sus.

2, 3, 6.

Chorus

(4. Shout) - sus. ('Cause) Your Name is po - wer, your name is

CCLI# 7136201

healing, your name____ is life.____ Break ev-'ry strong-hold, shine through the

Last time to Coda ⊕ | *1, 2.*   *D.C.* | *3.*   *D.S. al Coda*

sha-dows, burn like____ a fire.____ (4. Shout) a fire._____ Your name is

⊕ *Coda*

____ a fire._____ 1. I just want____ to speak____ the Name____ of Je-

-sus____ o-ver ev - 'ry heart__ and ev - 'ry mind. 'Cause

I know there__ is peace__ with-in__ your pre - sence, I speak Je - sus.____

I LOVE YOU LORD, OH YOUR MERCY NEVER FAILS ME
(GOODNESS OF GOD)

Key = A♭

Jenn Johnson, Ed Cash, Jason Ingram,
Ben Fielding & Brian Johnson

CCLI# 7117726

51

I RAISE A HALLELUJAH
(RAISE A HALLELUJAH)

hope will a-rise,   death is de-feat-ed,   the King—— is a-live.————— (I)

2a. I   Sing a lit-tle loud-er.—

(Sing a lit-tle loud-er.)—   Sing a lit-tle loud-er.——   (Sing a lit-tle loud-er.)—

Sing a lit-tle loud-er.——   (Sing a lit-tle loud-er.)—   Sing a lit-tle loud-er.——

(Sing a lit-tle loud-er.)—   Sing a lit-tle loud-er.——   In the pre-sence of my e-ne-mies.

Sing a lit-tle loud-er.__ Loud-er than my un-be-lief.__ Sing a lit tle loud er.__ My

wea-pon is a me-lo-dy.__ Sing a lit tle loud er.__ Hea - ven comes to fight for me.__

D.S. (with repeat) al Coda

Sing a lit-tle loud - er.__

✦ *Coda*   **Tag**

raise a hal-le-lu-jah,   I   raise a hal-le-lu-jah,   I

raise a hal-le-lu-jah,   I   raise a hal-le-lu - jah._____

essential
christian
presents

SONG
SOLUTIONS

essentialchristian.org

Copyright and Publishing for Christian Songwriters

Song Solutions is a music publisher and administrator specialising in Christian and Gospel music with over 25 years of experience in handling every aspect of copyright administration worldwide.

WRITERS

Have you written a song for the Church? Find out how we can help.

PUBLISHERS

We can get your songs and catalogues heard worldwide.

LICENSING

Require a license, or not sure which one you need? Get in touch!

Find out more at songsolutions.org or call 01825 748893

22

I REMEMBER WHAT YOU DID FOR ME
(I REMEMBER)

Key = E♭

Capo 1 (D)

Joth Hunt & Sam Evans

♩ = 74

CCLI# 7130990

57

NEW BIBLE STUDY RESOURCE

Through collective and responsive activities, this study looks at the seven characteristics that the church holds as it seeks to work out its mission in the world.

It encourages the reader to see how these characteristics are reflected in their own lives. Each session includes a Bible passage, key thoughts, reflective and action points as well as prayer suggestions.

I WAS LOST AND SEARCHED WITHIN
(HE IS ALIVE)

Key = Bm

Neal Glanville and Simon Brading

CCLI# 7134870

I'M CAUGHT UP IN YOUR PRESENCE
(NOTHING ELSE)

Key = C

Cody Carnes, Hank Bentley & Jessie Early

CCLI# 7123436

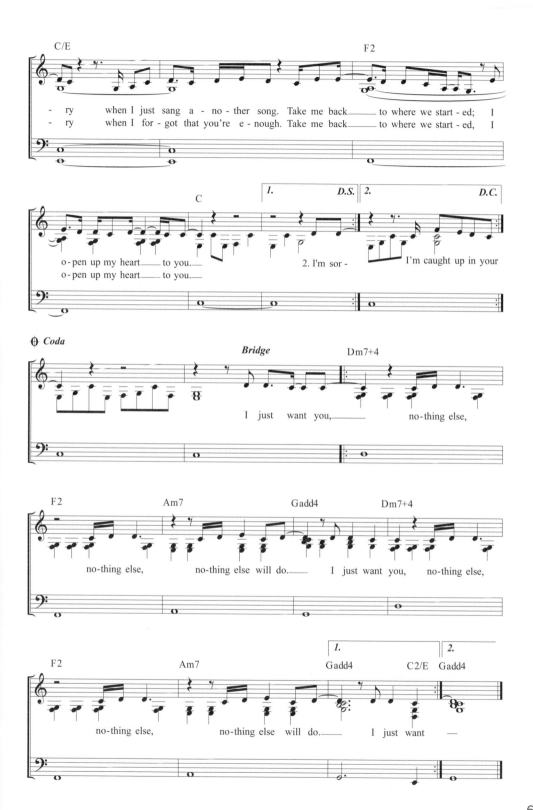

IN THE DARKNESS WE WERE WAITING
(KING OF KINGS)

Key = D

Brooke Ligertwood,
Jason Ingram & Scott Ligertwood

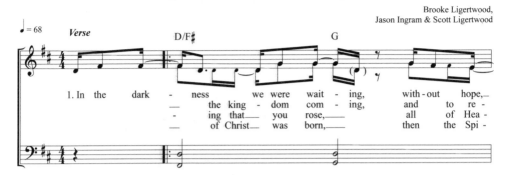

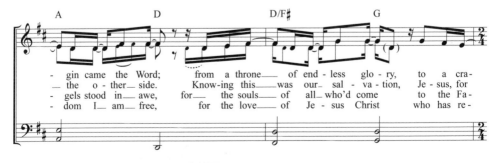

CCLI# 7127647

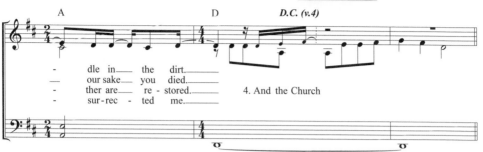

A   D   *D.C. (v.4)*

- dle in___ the dirt.___
- our sake___ you died.___
- ther are___ re - stored.___
- sur-rec - ted me.___

4. And the Church

Chorus

D   G2   Bm7   Asus4   A   D

Praise the Fa - ther, praise the Son,   praise the Spi - rit, Three in One.   God of glo - ry,

G2   Bm7   G2   *1, 2.*   A   D   *D.C.*

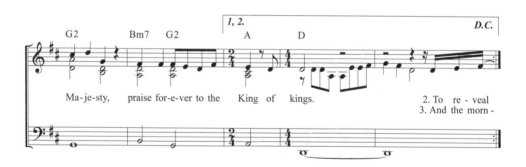

Ma-je-sty, praise for-e-ver to the   King of kings.

2. To re - veal
3. And the morn -

3.   **Outro**

A   D   D/F♯   G   A   D

King of kings. Praise for-e-ver to the   King of kings.

26

I'VE FOUND LIFE IN THE DESERT
(RIVER)

Key = C

Sam Archer & Simon Parkin

♩ = 140

Verse

1a. I've found life in the de - sert, I've seen love come pour-ing like the
1b. I've found peace in the val - ley, I've seen floods come ris-ing on the
2a. I've found grace in the dry lands, I've seen wa - ter fall-ing from on
life. 2b. I've found a hope and a fu - ture, I've seen love come pour-ing like the

1, 3. *2° D.C. (2b.)*

rain, wash-ing o - ver cracks like a ri - ver, dry bones com-ing back to life a-
plains, car - ry-ing the lost and the wea - ry, streams of
high, break-ing o - ver rocks like a foun-tain, Rush - ing in to bring me back to
rain, wash-ing o - ver cracks like a ri - ver, streams of

2, 4.

gain. love that can-not be con-

Chorus

- tained. A ri-ver of life has come

to me, a ri-ver of life has come to me, and I can see waves of li-

JUST LIKE YOU DID
IN DAYS OF OLD
(AS IT IS IN HEAVEN (REVIVAL FIRE))

Key = G

Kees Kraayenoord, Chris McClarney
& Matthijn Buwalda

Verse

1. Just like you did in days of old, come a - gain.
2. We've seen your Spi - rit move in pow'r, move a - gain.

And from the an - cient sto - ries told, rise a - gain.
Un - leash your church, this is the hour, rise a - gain.

Pre-Chorus

We need you, come heal our bro - ken land. We need you,

re - store us once a - gain. *Chorus* Re - vi - val fire,

stir out hearts with one de - sire to see your king - dom come on earth

CCLI# 7144590

28

JUST ONE WORD
(THERE'S NOTHING THAT OUR GOD CAN'T DO)

Key = A♭

Capo 1 (G)

♩ = 105

Brandon Lake, Kristian Stanfill & Jonathan Smith

1a. Just one word, you calm the storm that sur-rounds_____ me;_
1b. Just one touch, I feel the pre-sence of hea - ven;_
2a. Just one word, you heal what's bro-ken in - side_____ me;_
2b. Just one touch, I feel the po-wer of hea - ven;_

just one word, the dark-ness has to re-treat._
just one touch, my eyes were o-pened to see._
just one word, and you re-vive ev-'ry dream._
just one touch, my eyes were o-pened to see._

2nd time D.C. (2b.)

My heart can't help but be-lieve._____ 1. There's no-thing that our

God can't do; there's not a moun-tain that_____
God can't do; there's not a pri-son wall he

he can't move. } Oh, praise the_ name_____ that makes a_ way:_
can't break through. }

CCLI# 7141227

there's no-thing that our God can't do.

2. There's no-thing that our   I will be-lieve,   for great-er things,

there's no pow-er like the pow-er of Je - sus.___ Let faith a - rise,   let all a-gree,

there's no pow-er like the pow-er of Je - sus.   1. There's no-thing that our

KING OF HEAVEN, HOLY ONE
(WHAT A SAVIOUR)

Key = F♯

Capo 4 (D)

Anna Hamilton, Ben Cantelon,
Nick Herbert & Sam Bailey

CCLI# 7137905

LET EVERYTHING THAT HAS BREATH PRAISE THE LORD
(PRAISE THE LORD)

Key = F

LET PRAISE BE A WEAPON
(WE PRAISE YOU)

Key = D

Matt Redman, Brandon Lake,
Brian Johnson and Phil Wickham

LET THIS PLACE BE AN UPPER ROOM WHERE YOUR PEOPLE LEARN TO WAIT
(LET THERE BE WONDER)

Key = A

Matt Redman, Corey Voss,
Josh Silverberg & Jacob Sooter

1. Let this place be an up-per room where your peo-ple learn to wait. Let this house be-come
2. We're in awe, and we fear your name, but we will not be a-fraid. For the King in his

ho-ly ground where your chil-dren watch and pray. O, re-mind us to-day: we are
ho-li-ness is our Fa-ther and our friend. O, re-mind us to-day, we are

peo-ple of your pre-sence. Let there be won-der, let there be won-der in this
peo-ple of your pre-sence.

place. Let there be wor-ship, let there be wor-ship for your name. Come, Ho-ly

CCLI# 7138937

LIGHT IN THE DARKNESS, BEHELD THE DAWN OF DAYS
(I WILL EVER SING)

Key = A♭

Capo 1 (G)

Harvey Jessop & Pete James

CCLI# 7137186

essentialchristian.org

SPRING HARVEST 2020 THEME BOOK

The early church spread with remarkable speed, impelled by joy, urgency, profound compassion, and the day-to-day experience of working in the power of the Holy Spirit. Despite opposition at all levels, the first Christians expressed their love and wonder in acts of kindness, worship, and their eagerness to share the wholescale transformation that attends the profound experience of conversion.

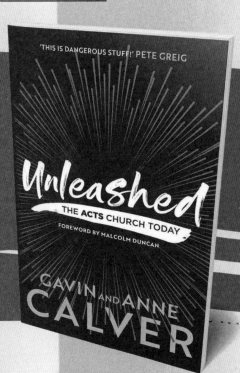

Gavin and Anne Calver explore what this extraordinary historical account means for believers today, considering themes including: The Holy Spirit in the life of the church; taking risks; living together in the power of the Spirit; works and wonders; hearing from God; responding to the call of God; miracles then and now.

LIGHT PIERCED THROUGH
THE DARK
(RISEN KING)

Key = B

CCLI# 7108555

MADE IN THIS WORLD BUT NOT MADE OF IT
(LORD OF MY LIFE)

Key = Gm

Lucy Grimble

CCLI# 7071948

85

MAGNIFICENT, MARVELOUS, MATCHLESS LOVE

Key = D

Matt Papa, Aaron Keyes, Keith Getty, Kristyn Getty & Luke Brown

CCLI# 7119246

MERCY EVERY MORNING, RISING LIKE THE DAWN
(UP AND ALIVE)

Key = A

Luke Hellebronth, Anna Hellebronth,
Jimmy James & David Ostby

♩ = 92 *Verse*

A
1. Mer - cy ev - 'ry morn - ing, ris - ing like the dawn;
2. You can still the pa - nic, you can break the chains;

Dmaj7
God of all cre - a - tion, the won - der of it all.
you're the on - ly heal - er, the great - est e - ver name.

A
You're the song of free - dom, You're the on - ly way;
Through the cross for - gi - ven, ev - 'ry - thing has changed,

F♯m7   **Esus**   *Chorus* 𝄋 **A**
ev - 'ry new be - gin - ning is by grace. Up and a - live in Je - sus, in
ev - 'ry new be - gin - ning is by grace. from the grave you raised me, out

F♯m7   **1, 3. D2**
- to a life of free - dom, hal - le - lu - jah, Christ is ri - sen. Up
of the dark - ness saved me, hal - le - lu - jah,

CCLI# 7122400

38

O FOR A CLOSER WALK WITH GOD
(MARTYRDOM)

Key = E

Colin Webster, Hugh Wilson & William Cowper

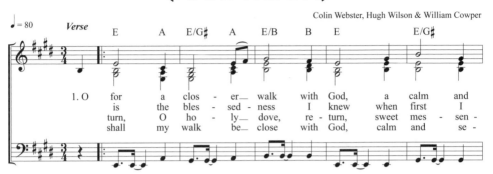

1. O for a clos - er walk with God, a calm and
   is the bles - sed - ness I knew when first I
   turn, O ho - ly dove, re - turn, sweet mes - sen -
   shall my walk be close with God, calm and se -

heav'n - ly frame; a light to shine up - on the
saw the Lord; where is the soul re - fresh - ing
ger of rest; I hate the sins that made thee
rene my frame; so pur - er light shall mark the

1, 4.
(Fine)

road that leads me to the Lamb.
view of Je - sus and his
mourn, and drove thee from my
road that leads me to the Lamb!

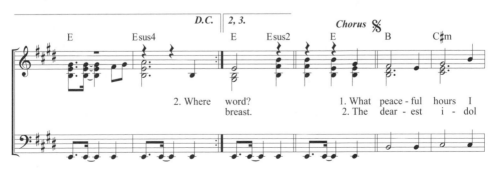

D.C. 2, 3.   Chorus

2. Where word?   1. What peace - ful hours I
   breast.   2. The dear - est i - dol

CCLI# 7133096

once en - joyed, how sweet their_ mem - 'ry still;_____ but they have
I have known, what - e'er that_ i - dol be;_____ help me to

left an ach - ing void the world____ can_ ne - ver
tear it from thy throne, and wor - ship____ on - ly

1, 3.   *D.C. (al Fine)* **2.**   *D.S*

fill_____ 3. Re - thee.   2. The
thee._____ 4. Then

OH GOD, HOW COULD I STAND
(GREAT REDEEMER)

Key = F

Lucy Grimble

CCLI# 7096881

OH THE MYSTERY
(THIS IS LOVE)

Key = A♭

Chris Sayburn, Daniel Cox,
David Ostby & Sem Schaap

CCLI# 7133203

OH YAHWEH, MY HEART IS YOURS
(CREATED TO WORSHIP)

Key = D

Lucy Grimble

CCLI# 7071949

Last time to Coda ⊕ | 1. | | 3. | D.S. al Coda | 2.
D/F♯

like Da - vid a king yet so un - re-strained.___

Bridge
G2   D/F♯   A   Bm7

Flesh and bone_ yet e - ter - nal,   you've cho - sen this earth - en ves - sel,

G2   Em7   Bm7 A   G2   D/F♯

to bring glo - ry to_ your name.___   With ev-'ry fi - bre, with all_ that I_ am,

A   Bm7   Em7   D   1.
A

I will de-clare, I will shout your praise out,   to bring glo - ry to_ your name.___

2, 3.   D.S. ⊕ Coda
A   A   D

42

PIERCING THROUGH THE DARK, YOU SHINE YOUR LIGHT
(OVERFLOW)

Key = Dm

Ysabel Bain, Simon Brading, Jess Debenham,
Rachel Fellingham & Larissa Matson

1. Pierc - ing through the dark, you shine your light; when you breathe in - to the dust we come a - live. Speak-ing in - to life all your de - sign, this is who you are and we're rea - dy for you.
2. We have seen your mi - ra - cles and might; seen the po - wer of your king-dom in our lives. Break-ing ev - 'ry chain that ties and binds, this is who you are and we're rea - dy for you.
3. Bro - ken hearts are mend - ed and re - stored; you re - deem all things to bet - ter than be - fore. Till ev - 'ry knee will bow be - fore your throne, this is who you are and your pro - mise is true.

Pre-Chorus

you rule and you reign, o - ver ev - 'ry-thing you're sov - 'reign.

We long for your glo - ry, for more of you. We want to see your king-dom

CCLI# 7134865

come on earth; we want to see your Spi-rit move on earth. Oh Fa-ther, let your will be

2nd time D.S.S repeat Chorus   *1st time D.C. (v.3)*

done on earth____ as in Hea - ven.__

Bridge   *Repeat ad lib: D.S. (with repeats) al Fine*

O - ver-flow.__ O - ver-flow.__ O - ver-flow.____

Dm *(Fine)*

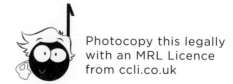

43

SENT BY THE FATHER, JESUS HAS COME
(SENT BY THE FATHER)

Key = D

Words: Tim Chester
Additional Words & Music: Colin Webster & Phil Moore

Verse

1. Sent by the Fa - ther,— Je - sus has come, splen - dour of Hea - ven,— glo - ri - ous Son. Com - ing to suf - fer,— com - ing to save, Ris - ing in tri - umph o - ver the grave.
2. Sent by the Sa - viour,— Spi - rit of life, sent to re - veal the— glo - ries of Christ. Come to your peo - ple,— come and in - spire, fill - ing our lives with— mis - sion - 'ry fire.
3. Sent by the Lord of— Hea - ven and Earth, tell - ing the world his— glo - ri - ous worth. We are his peo - ple,— him we pro - claim, mak - ing di - sci - ples— in Je - sus' name.

Chorus

Let us go in the po - wer of the Lord; bring the gos - pel to ev - 'ry tribe and tongue. Let us go for the ho - nour of our God, let us go for the glo - ry of the Son.

Last time D.S.

D.C.

THE HOLY ONE HAS JUST WALKED IN
(THE HOLY ONE)

Key = B

Sam Archer, Josh Fraser,
Fiona Fraser & Stefan Cashwell

Capo 4 (G)

103

THE LORD IS MY SHEPHERD, HE GOES BEFORE ME
(PSALM 23 (I AM NOT ALONE))

Key = E

Joshua Sherman, Steven Musso,
Laurel Taylor & The Emerging Sound

CCLI# 7111981

105

THE MORE I BEHOLD YOU
(CAN'T TAKE MY EYES OFF YOU)

Key = D♭

Capo 1 (C)

Mitch Wong & Andy Harrison

♪ = 154

CCLI# 7134789

THERE IS A THRONE
WITH RAINBOW COLOURS
BLAZING ALL AROUND
(HOLY IS THE NAME)

Key = G

Olly Knight, Tom James & Pete Szczerbicki

CCLI# 7096890

Ho - ly is the name of the___ Lord.
Wor - thy is the name of the___ Lord.

Ho - ly is the name of the__
Wor - thy is the name of the__

Last time to Coda ⊕ | 1, 2.

___Lord, who was and is to___ come,
___Lord, all pow'r and praise be___ yours.

who was and is to come.

D.C. ‖ 3. *D.S.S. (Ch. 2)*

2. Be - hold the__
3. And there I'll__

⊕ *Coda*

All pow'r and praise be yours.

THERE IS NO ONE LIKE YOU, JESUS SON OF GOD
(PRAISES TO THE ONE)

Key = B♭

Capo 3 (G)

Sam Archer, Simon Parkin & Josh Fraser

THIS JESUS THAT CARRIED
OUR SHAME
(THE SAME JESUS)

Key = A

Jacob Sooter,
Josh Silverberg & Matt Redman

Verse lyrics:

1. This Je - sus, that car - ried our shame; this Je - sus, who rose from the grave, the same Je - sus we wor - ship to - day, we wor - ship to - day.

2. Came to us, with grace and in truth; still with us, and still on the move, the same Je - sus, he is mak - ing us new, he is mak - ing us new.

3. He's com - mand - ing the wind and the waves; his king - dom for - e - ver shall reign. We know that he is com - ing a gain, he is com - ing a - gain.

I know that my Re-

CCLI# 7138933

deem - er lives; I know that my Re - deem - er lives.

he's still keep - ing all his pro - mi - ses; the same Je - sus,

3rd time D.S. al Coda
Last time to Coda ⊕   *Interlude*

the same Je - sus. Woah._____ Woah._____

(1st time to v.3)   *Bridge*

Oh, he's the First and the Last, the Be - gin - ning and

End; at the sound of his cry all the world came a - live. And he formed us from

dust, put his breath in our lungs; we were made for his love, but we ran from the

light. But he would-n't give up on his daugh-ters and sons, so he took on the

cross, and he laid down his life. And he did what he said, when he rose from the

D.S. ⊕ Coda   *Interlude*

dead, and he's com-ing back a - gain._____ Woah._____

_____ Woah._____

essential christian

essentialchristian.org

Your Local Primary School Needs You!!

Does your church have a mission to children?

Would your church be willing to sponsor a local Primary School with a Big Start Assembly subscription and assist them by running an assembly?

If the answer is yes why not...

- TRY TWO FREE ASSEMBLIES now with no sign up or commitment
- 30% Off Annual Subscription
- Free use of material by church sponsoring the school

Every school has to hold a time of Collective Worship providing every KS1 and KS2 child with an opportunity to hear about God and explore the Christian faith. However, without the right material and the guidance and assistance of local churches this is a difficult task for most schools.

Big Start Assemblies comes with 124 ready to use assemblies for Collective Worship packed with assembly plans, songs, multimedia, PowerPoint. slides and much, much more...

Assembly

Prophecies of Jesus: Jesus' Life

Today's story is the second in a series exploring prophecies about Jesus found in the Old Testament book of Isaiah. Around 700 years before Jesus actually started living out the...

View

#Hope

Assembly

Giants of Faith: Esther

This assembly explores how Esther, a poor, orphan, Jewish girl became Queen. Esther kept her Jewish heritage quiet until she heard from her Uncle that there had been a plot planned to kill all the Jews, and...

View

#Courage

Find out more by visiting
www.bigstartassemblies.org

115

50

TO SEE THE OUTCAST ACCEPTED
(SEND REVIVAL)

Key = G

Ian Yates & Sam Blake

♩ = 70 **Verse**

1. To see the out-cast ac-cep-ted, to see the cap-tive run-ning
2. To see the wound-ed find their heal-ing, to see the lone-ly find a
3. To see the bride know her true worth, to see her stand-ing as
4. Move us past en-ter-tain-ment, move us be-yond our un-be-

— free, to see the hope-less have a pur-pose,
— home, to see the bro-ken find com-fort,
— one, to see her flou-rish-ing in free-dom,
- lief, lead us now to full sur-ren-der,

Last time to Coda

1. C2

O to see your king-dom come.
(4.) O lead us to our

2, 3. C2 — come.

Chorus

Lord send re-

G D C2

vi - val, start with me. Lord send re-

G D/A

1, 5. C2

D.C. (v.3, v.4)

vi - val, start with me.

CCLI# 7136990

51

WE ARE THE BRIDE AND
WE ARE WAITING
(IN WONDER)

Key = C

Kees Kraayenoord, Travis Ryan & Matthijn Buwalda

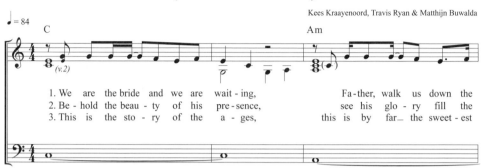

1. We are the bride and we are wait - ing,   Fa - ther, walk us down the
2. Be - hold the beau - ty of his pre - sence,   see his glo - ry fill the
3. This is the sto - ry of the a - ges,   this is by far the sweet - est

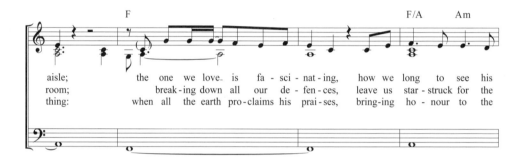

aisle;   the one we love is fa - sci - nat - ing,   how we long to see his
room;   break - ing down all our de - fen - ces,   leave us star - struck for the
thing: when all the earth pro - claims his prai - ses,   bring - ing ho - nour to the

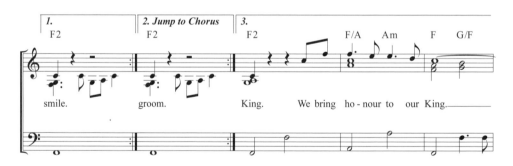

1.
2. Jump to Chorus
3.

smile.   groom.   King.   We bring ho - nour to our King.

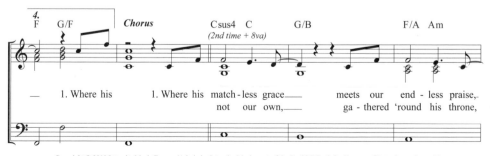

4.
Chorus
(2nd time + 8va)

— 1. Where his   1. Where his match - less grace   meets our end - less praise,
not our own,   ga - thered 'round his throne,

WERE CREATION SUDDENLY ARTICULATE
(CHRIST BE MAGNIFIED)

Key = A

Cody Carnes, Cory Asbury
& Ethan Hulse

CCLI# 7139866

WHEN I ONCE WAS LOST
(HAVE YOUR WAY)

Key = B♭

Lucy Taylor, Taylor & Co

Capo 3 (D) *Verse*

1. When I once was lost: emp-ty, bro-ken, bound;

Hid-den in my fear, you struck, the walls came down. 2. Your

love went deep-er still; found my heart, set it a-light. The
3. Set the cap-tives free; grace be-yond im-pos-si-ble. Still

flames were burst-ing out, love has won, now I'm a-live. 1. We lift you
mer-cy we re-ceive, and love so im-mea-sura-ble.

high-er, high-er. Our God is strong-er, strong-
po-wer, po-wer, he's death de-feat-ing, he is strong-

- er. Your love can't be tar-nished, your light can't be dark-ened, we sing your praise.
- er. Our chains have been bro-ken, his grace is— our free-dom, we sing your praise.

1. We lift you Je-sus,— have— your way.

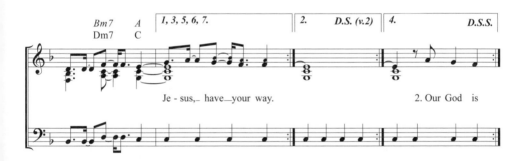

Je - sus,— have—your way.

2. Our God is

54

WHEN THE WORD OF GOD WAS FIRST HEARD ON EARTH
(WHEN THE WORD OF GOD)

Key = C

Phil Moore & Tim Chester

1. When the Word of God was first heard on earth, each hill and dale with love was drawn, and the darkness fled, the chaos dispersed; from the emptiness all life was born.

Word of God to the prophets came, the Spirit breathed through ev'ry page. So each word and phrase now carries Christ's name, and his glory shines from age to age.

Word of God in the cradle lay, God's love was clothed in human flesh. The eternal Word through whom all was made, came into his world and took a breath.

Word of God made this world his home, he calmed the storms and stilled the waves. Melted hearts that once had been made of stone, spoke with words of life and emptied graves.

Word of God comes to us today, may emptiness be turned to praise. May our darkest fears be driven away, as our glorious Saviour fills our gaze.

Chorus
Come, let us hear your precious voice,

CCLI# 7117665

and send us out with hearts re - joic - ing. All who have ears, come let us

hear how great, how great is our God.

1, 2.   D.C.   3.   D.S.

3. When the   Come, let us
5. As the

4.

Photocopy this legally
with an MRL Licence
from ccli.co.uk

WHEN WE LEAST EXPECT IT YOU ARRIVE
(COME SURPRISE US)

Key = C

Matthijn Buwalda, Kees Kraayenoord,
Corey Voss & Rhyan Shirley

CCLI# 7125786

WHEN YOU APPEAR, OUR LIVES ARE CHANGED
(JESUS VICTORIOUS)

Key = G

Kees Kraayenoord, Eline Bakker & Reyer Van Drongelen

CCLI# 7133798

Cmaj7   Dsus4 D   G2   *Chorus* 𝄋 Gsus4   G

— is high-er, Lord— of all.   Oh King— of kings, you will

D/F♯   Em   Gsus4   G   Em7   Dsus4   D

reign——— on high,— for - e — ver and glo - ri - ous.—

C   Dsus4   Em   G/B   *Last time to Coda* ⊕   C   D

No-thing can— with-stand the po— wer of—your migh-ty name: Je-sus,— vic-to-ri-

1.   G2   *D.C.*   2.   G   C/E   D/F♯   *D.S.*   3.   G

ous.   3. Your love and light   ous.   Oh   ous.

Bridge   G   D/F♯

No o-ther name——— is high - er.   No o-ther name—

129

Experts In Event Solutions

EVENT MANAGEMENT

TICKETING

DELEGATE REGISTRATION

EXHIBITION PLANNING AND MANAGEMENT

HEALTH & SAFETY

TECHNICAL MANAGEMENT

RECORDING & DUPLICATION

visit **www.eem.solutions** to find out more

YOU ARE HERE, MOVING IN OUR MIDST
(WAY MAKER)

Key = E

Osinachi Kalu Okoro Egbu

CCLI# 7115744

2, 4. C#m   **D.C. (v.2,3)** B   **6, 8.** C#m   **Tag**   A

are.   2. You are here,   are.   That is who you_ are.   that is who you_

E/G#   B   **1, 3.** C#m

are.   that is who you_ are.   that is who you_ are.   that is who you_

2, 4. C#m *(Fine)*   **Bridge (3°,4° 8va.)** A

are.   E - ven when I don't see it, you're work - ing.

E   Bsus4

E - ven when I don't feel it, you're work - ing.   you ne - ver stop, you ne - ver stop work - ing.

(Repeat 4 times then D.S. al Fine)

C#m

you ne - ver stop,   you ne - ver stop work - ing.

133

58

YOU ARE THE RIVER THAT WON'T RUN DRY
(YOUR WILL, YOUR WAY)

Key = G♭m

Capo 4 (D)

Bryan Torwalt, Hank Bentley,
Katie Torwalt & Phil Wickham

Verse

1. You are the ri-ver that won't run dry, there is no de-sert your streams won't find; wher-e-ver it runs hearts come a-live, ri-ver, flow through me, ri-ver, flow through me.

2. You are the fi-re that can't be tamed; there is no dark your light can't break. Breathe on the coals, come stir up the flame; fi-re burn in me, fi-re burn in me.

Chorus

(hearts) Your will, your way, do what-e-ver you want to; come move come reign, let your king-dom in-vade our hearts.

(D.S. Last Chorus repeat)
Last time to Coda

CCLI# 7127217

59

YOUR BLOOD IS HEALING EV'RY WOUND
(BETTER WORD)

Key = B

Jack Mooring,
Kyle Lee & Leeland Mooring

CCLI# 7130729

YOUR LOVE CAME FIRST
(I WILL PRAISE YOU)

Key = C

Ben Fielding, Joel Houston,
Matt Crocker & Dylan Thomas

CCLI# 7135002

139

springharvest.org

We need you!

Join our amazing team of volunteers.

Find out about volunteering opportunities at Spring Harvest.

GUITAR CHORDS

A good chord vocabulary is essential for a guitarist to feel confident when playing in worship, especially when the situation may involve reading a previously unseen piece of music or picking up a song quickly by ear. The chords on these pages are arranged in 'families' according to key.

This is a beneficial way of remembering chords as most songs stick to these groupings. For each key, the first row shows the simplest form of each chord and the second line gives a more interesting substitution. The third line shows the chords most commonly used by guitarists derived by keeping some sort of pedal tone ringing in each chord and the fourth line shows inverted chords with an alternate bass note.

Also included are the Roman Numerals and Nashville Numbers associated with each chord. If you've not come across these before, they are simply an easy way of numbering each chord within a key. This is useful as it means you can take any chord progression in one key and instantly transpose it to another. Furthermore you can try out any of the chords in each column that corresponds to the relevant Roman Numeral and see if there is chord type or inversion which still fits but adds a different flavour. Experimentation like this may open up creative chord progressions that serve as a catalyst to help you to worship in fresh ways or to write new songs.

Roman	I	II	III	IV	V	VI	VII
Nashville	1	2	3	4	5	6	7
3-note chord (triad)	C	Dm	Em	F	G	Am	Bdim
4-note chord	C maj7	D m7	E m7	F maj7	G7	A m7	Bm7♭5
Alternative substitute	C	D7sus4	E m7	F sus2	G5	A m7	Dsus4/B
Alternative bass note	C/E	Dm/F	Em/G	F/A	F/G	A m/E	

Key of C

For all chords in the key of C# or Db, use the chords from the key of C with capo 1

141

GUITAR CHORDS

	Roman	I	II	III	IV	V	VI	VII
	Nashville	1	2	3	4	5	6	7
Key of D	3-note chord (triad)	D	Em	F#m	G	A	Bm	C#dim
	4-note chord	Dmaj7	Em7	F#m7	Gmaj7	A7	Bm7	C#m7♭5
	Alternative substitute	Dsus2	Em9	F#m7	G6sus2	A7sus4	Bm11	Aadd9/C#
	Alternative bass note	D/F#	Em/B	F#m/A	G/B	G/A	Bm/F#	

For all chords in the key of D# or E♭, use the chords from the key of D with capo 1

		I	II	III	IV	V	VI	VII
Key of E	3-note chord (triad)	E	F#m	G#m	A	B	C#m	D#dim
	4-note chord	Emaj7	F#m7	G#m7	Amaj7	B7	C#m7	D#m7♭5
	Alternative substitute	E5	F#m11	G#madd♭6	Aadd9	Badd4	C#m7	D#alt
	Alternative bass note	E/G#	F#m/C#	G#m/D#	A/C#	A/B	C#m/G#	

For all chords in the key of F, use the chords from the key of E with capo 1

For all chords in the key of F# or Gb, use the chords from the key of E with capo 2

GUITAR CHORDS

Roman	I	II	III	IV	V	VI	VII
Nashville	1	2	3	4	5	6	7

Key of G

	I	II	III	IV	V	VI	VII
3-note chord (triad)	G	A m	B m	C	D	E m	F#dim
4-note chord	G maj7	A m7	B m7	C maj7	D7	E m7	F#m7♭5
Alternative substitute	G	A 7sus4	Dsus4/B	Cadd9	Dsus4	E m7	G/F#
Alternative bass note	G/D	A m/C	Bm/D	C/G	C/D	Em/G	

For all chords in the key of G# or A♭, use the chords from the key of G with capo 1

Key of A

	I	II	III	IV	V	VI	VII
3-note chord (Triad)	A	Bm	C#m	D	E	F#m	G#dim
4-note chord	A maj7	B m7	C#m7	D maj7	E7	F#m7	G#m7♭5
Alternative substitute	A sus2	Bsus4	C#m7	D6sus2	Eadd9	F#m11	Eadd9/G#
Alternative bass note	A/E	Bm/F#	C#m/E	D/A	D/E	F#m/A	

For all chords in the key of A# or Bb, use the chords from the key of A with capo 1

For all chords in the key of B, use the chords from the key of A with capo 2

143

SCRIPTURE INDEX

136:1	I love you Lord, oh your mercy never fails me
136:1	There is no one like you, Jesus son of God
143:1	Here in this moment you are able
143:10	Holy Spirit, guide my vision
145:3	Fill my lungs with the wind of your Spirit
145:3	The Holy One has just walked in
145:7	Magnificent, marvelous, matchless love
145:7	We are the bride and we are waiting
146:6	This Jesus that carried our shame
148:13	King of Heaven, Holy one
148:13	Light in the darkness, beheld the dawn of days
150:6	Let everything that has breath praise the Lord
150:6	Oh Yahweh, my heart is yours

ISAIAH
6:1	To see the outcast accepted
6:3	There is a throne with rainbow colours blazing all around
6:3	We are the bride and we are waiting
9:6	Oh Yahweh, my heart is yours
32:3	When the Word of God was first heard on earth
33:2	Eternal Father, gracious King
33:2	For what we have done and left undone
35:6	You are the river that won't run dry
43:16	You are here, moving in our midst
46:9	There is no one like you, Jesus son of God
46:9	Your love came first
61:1	When I once was lost
61:10	Your blood is healing ev'ry wound
63:7	I remember what you did for me

JEREMIAH
| 10:6 | There is no one like you, Jesus son of God |
| 31:4 | Oh Yahweh, my heart is yours |

LAMENTATIONS
| 3:22-23 | There is no one like you, Jesus son of God |

EZEKIEL
| 37:5 | I've found life in the desert |

DANIEL
| 4:37 | King of Heaven, Holy one |

JOEL
| 2:21 | Come let us worship our King |

MICAH
| 6:8 | Made in this world but not made of it |

MATTHEW
2:15	He who was before there was light
5:16	Did you know, did you know
6:10	Just like you did in days of old
6:10	Piercing through the dark, you shine your light
6:10	You are the river that won't run dry
11:15	When the Word of God was first heard on earth
11:28-29	Come like you want to
19:26	Just one word
20:31	Eternal Father, gracious King
20:31	For what we have done and left undone
26:26	Are you hurting and broken within
28:4-6	God, you brought us out of the wilderness
28:19	Sent by the Father, Jesus has come

MARK
6:15	Sent by the Father, Jesus has come
9:10	He who was before there was light
9:24	To see the outcast accepted
9:29	I'm caught up in your presence

LUKE
1:37	Just one word
4:18	Come and see the King
4:18	To see the outcast accepted
4:18	When I once was lost
5:29	He who was before there was light
10:39	I'm caught up in your presence
11:2	Just like you did in days of old
11:2	Piercing through the dark, you shine your light
11:2	You are the river that won't run dry
15:24	I was lost and searched within
16:26	How great the chasm that lay between us
19:10	When I once was lost
24:1-8	In the darkness we were waiting

JOHN
1:5	Light in the darkness, beheld the dawn of days
1:5	Light pierced through the dark
1:5	Piercing through the dark, you shine your light
1:5	You are the river that won't run dry
1:14	The more I behold you
1:14	This Jesus that carried our shame
4:7	Are you hurting and broken within
4:10	I've found life in the desert
6:69	The Holy One has just walked in
7:38	I've found life in the desert
9:39	Come and see the King
10:2	Your blood is healing ev'ry wound
14:6	You are here, moving in our midst
14:16	Did you know, did you know
14:27	O for a closer walk with God
15:13	King of Heaven, Holy one
16:13	Holy Spirit, guide my vision
16:13	Oh the mystery

ACTS

2:2-4	Come Holy Spirit, fill us now
2:3	Just like you did in days of old
2:3	Let this place be an upper room where your people learn to wait
2:4	Did you know, did you know
2:24	I was lost and searched within
2:24-28	In the darkness we were waiting
2:42-47	In the darkness we were waiting
4:12	Come and see the King
13:13	I remember what you did for me
19:5	I just want to speak the Name of Jesus

ROMANS

5:5	Come Holy Spirit, fill us now
5:9	Amazing love! How can it be
8:10	I just want to speak the Name of Jesus
8:15	Eternal Father, gracious King
11:6	Magnificent, marvelous, matchless love
12:1	Are you hurting and broken within
14:9	Amazing love! How can it be

1 CORINTHIANS

3:11	Oh God, how could I stand
13:12	The Lord is my Shepherd, he goes before me
15:20	Light pierced through the dark
15:54	Light pierced through the dark
15:55	When you appear, our lives are changed
15:55-57	Come let us worship our King
15:56	Oh the mystery
15:57	I remember what you did for me
15:57	The Lord is my Shepherd, he goes before me

2 CORINTHIANS

3:17	King of Heaven, Holy one
3:17	Mercy every morning, rising like the dawn
3:17	The more I behold you
4:9	Let this place be an upper room where your people learn to wait
5:14-15	Amazing love! How can it be
9:8	Here in this moment you are able

GALATIANS

2:20	Arise my soul
4:6	Eternal Father, gracious King
5:1	How great the chasm that lay between us

EPHESIANS

1:6	Let praise be a weapon
1:7	How great the chasm that lay between us
1:7	Your blood is healing ev'ry wound
3:17-19	Let everything that has breath praise the Lord
5:9	Did you know, did you know

PHILIPPIANS

2:7	Come and see the King
2:9	Come and see the King
2:9	Light in the darkness, beheld the dawn of days
2:9	Made in this world but not made of it
2:9	There is no one like you, Jesus son of God
2:10	Piercing through the dark, you shine your light
2:10	When you appear, our lives are changed
2:6-8	Amazing love! How can it be
2:9-11	Were creation suddenly articulate
4:7	Here in this moment you are able

COLOSSIANS

1:13-14	Mercy every morning, rising like the dawn
1:18	Did you know, did you know

1 THESSALONIANS

2:16	Fill my lungs with the wind of your Spirit
2:16	Magnificent, marvelous, matchless love

1 TIMOTHY

1:10	Light pierced through the dark
6:15	When you appear, our lives are changed

2 TIMOTHY

1:10	I raise a hallelujah
1:10	When I once was lost

TITUS

3:4	How great the chasm that lay between us
3:5	I was lost and searched within

HEBREWS

2:12	Oh Yahweh, my heart is yours
2:14	I was lost and searched within
2:14	Sent by the Father, Jesus has come
4:12	When the Word of God was first heard on earth
4:16	Eternal Father, gracious King
7:27	King of Heaven, Holy one
12:1	Made in this world but not made of it
12:1	The more I behold you
12:2	Amazing love! How can it be
12:2	Come like you want to
13:15	I just want to speak the Name of Jesus
13:15	Let everything that has breath praise the Lord
13:20-21	You are the river that won't run dry

JAMES

1:2	Are you hurting and broken within

1 PETER

1:3	How great the chasm that lay between us
1:19	Eternal Father, gracious King
1:19	Oh God, how could I stand
1:20	Come Holy Spirit, fill us now
5:1	Are you hurting and broken within
5:6	I'm caught up in your presence

2 PETER

1:16	When we least expect it you arrive

1 JOHN

1:7	Oh God, how could I stand
2:1	For what we have done and left undone
3:19	I'm caught up in your presence
4:14	O for a closer walk with God
5:1	Come and see the King

JUDE

1:25	Oh the mystery

REVELATION

1:5	How great the chasm that lay between us
1:5	Your blood is healing ev'ry wound
1:8	He who was before there was light
1:8	There is a throne with rainbow colours blazing all around
1:8	Your love came first
1:18	I was lost and searched within
2:4	O for a closer walk with God
3:3	When we least expect it you arrive
3:21	When you appear, our lives are changed
4:1-11	There is a throne with rainbow colours blazing all around
4:8	From life's beginning
4:8	He who was before there was light
4:8	We are the bride and we are waiting
5:12	He who was before there was light
11:15	I remember what you did for me
17:7	I remember what you did for me
19:1	Come and see the King
19:1	I raise a hallelujah
19:1	I've found life in the desert
19:7	Let praise be a weapon
19:7	We are the bride and we are waiting
19:16	When you appear, our lives are changed
21:1	Are you hurting and broken within
21:4	I remember what you did for me
21:5	This Jesus that carried our shame
21:5	When we least expect it you arrive
21:5	Your blood is healing ev'ry wound
21:6	Your love came first
22:4	The Lord is my Shepherd, he goes before me
22:4-5	God, you brought us out of the wilderness
22:5	I remember what you did for me
22:13	Your love came first
22:20	This Jesus that carried our shame
22:20	To see the outcast accepted

THEMATIC INDEX

CALL TO WORSHIP

Always true, always kind
Arise my soul
Come and see the King
Come let us worship our King
From life's beginning
He who was before there was light
Let everything that has breath praise the Lord
Let praise be a weapon
There is no one like you, Jesus son of God
Were creation suddenly articulate
When the Word of God was first heard on earth
You are here, moving in our midst

THE CHURCH, THE PEOPLE OF GOD

Did you know, did you know
From life's beginning
In the darkness we were waiting
Just like you did in days of old
Let this place be an upper room where your people learn to wait
Sent by the Father, Jesus has come
To see the outcast accepted
We are the bride and we are waiting
Were creation suddenly articulate

COME LORD JESUS - THE PRESENCE OF GOD

Come Holy Spirit, fill us now
Come like you want to
I just want to speak the Name of Jesus
I'm caught up in your presence
I've found life in the desert
Just like you did in days of old
Just one word
Let this place be an upper room where your people learn to wait
O for a closer walk with God
Piercing through the dark, you shine your light
The Holy One has just walked in
The more I behold you
We are the bride and we are waiting
When we least expect it you arrive
When you appear, our lives are changed
You are the river that won't run dry

COMMUNION
(SEE ALSO JESUS - CROSS AND RESURRECTION)

Amazing love! How can it be
For what we have done and left undone
I remember what you did for me
King of Heaven, Holy one
Oh God, how could I stand

CONFESSION

Amazing love! How can it be
Are you hurting and broken within
Eternal Father, gracious King
For what we have done and left undone
I was lost and searched within
I'm caught up in your presence
O for a closer walk with God
To see the outcast accepted

CREATION

From life's beginning
He who was before there was light
Let everything that has breath praise the Lord
Light in the darkness, beheld the dawn of days
Light pierced through the dark
Magnificent, marvelous, matchless love
This Jesus that carried our shame
Were creation suddenly articulate
When the Word of God was first heard on earth

DEDICATION AND COMMITMENT

Amazing love! How can it be
Arise my soul
Holy Spirit, guide my vision
I love you Lord, oh your mercy never fails me
I've found life in the desert
Made in this world but not made of it
O for a closer walk with God
Oh the mystery
Oh Yahweh, my heart is yours
Were creation suddenly articulate
Your love came first

FAITH AND TRUST

Always true, always kind
Come and see the King
Come Holy Spirit, fill us now
Come like you want to
Fill my lungs with the wind of your Spirit
Here in this moment you are able
Holy Spirit, guide my vision
I raise a hallelujah
Just one word
Let praise be a weapon
Let this place be an upper room where your people learn to wait
This Jesus that carried our shame
You are here, moving in our midst
You are the river that won't run dry

FAMILY WORSHIP

Did you know, did you know
Oh Yahweh, my heart is yours

GOD, LORD AND FATHER

Are you hurting and broken within
Come like you want to
Eternal Father, gracious King
For what we have done and left undone
God, you brought us out of the wilderness
He who was before there was light
I love you Lord, oh your mercy never fails me
When you appear, our lives are changed

GOD'S LOVE AND FAITHFULNESS

Come let us worship our King
God, you brought us out of the wilderness
I love you Lord, oh your mercy never fails me
I remember what you did for me
King of Heaven, Holy one
Let everything that has breath praise the Lord
Light in the darkness, beheld the dawn of days
Magnificent, marvelous, matchless love
Oh God, how could I stand
When I once was lost
When you appear, our lives are changed
Your love came first

GUIDANCE AND DIRECTION

Here in this moment you are able
Holy Spirit, guide my vision
I love you Lord, oh your mercy never fails me
O for a closer walk with God
The Lord is my Shepherd, he goes before me

HEALING

Come Holy Spirit, fill us now
Come like you want to
Here in this moment you are able
Just one word
Let this place be an upper room where your people learn to wait
Mercy every morning, rising like the dawn
Piercing through the dark, you shine your light
The more I behold you
We are the bride and we are waiting
You are here, moving in our midst
Your blood is healing ev'ry wound

HEART WORSHIP

Are you hurting and broken within
Fill my lungs with the wind of your Spirit
God, you brought us out of the wilderness
I love you Lord, oh your mercy never fails me
I've found life in the desert
Just one word
Let this place be an upper room where your people learn to wait
Light in the darkness, beheld the dawn of days
Made in this world but not made of it
Mercy every morning, rising like the dawn
Oh the mystery
Oh Yahweh, my heart is yours
The Holy One has just walked in
The more I behold you
There is a throne with rainbow colours blazing all around
There is no one like you, Jesus son of God
We are the bride and we are waiting
Were creation suddenly articulate
You are here, moving in our midst
Your love came first

HEAVEN AND THE PROMISE OF ETERNITY

Come Holy Spirit, fill us now
God, you brought us out of the wilderness
Light pierced through the dark
Made in this world but not made of it
There is a throne with rainbow colours blazing all around
We are the bride and we are waiting
Were creation suddenly articulate

HOLY SPIRIT

Come and see the King
Come Holy Spirit, fill us now
Did you know, did you know
Fill my lungs with the wind of your Spirit
Holy Spirit, guide my vision
Let this place be an upper room where your
people learn to wait
O for a closer walk with God
The Holy One has just walked in
The Lord is my Shepherd, he goes before me
When we least expect it you arrive
You are the river that won't run dry

JESUS - CROSS AND RESURRECTION

Amazing love! How can it be
Are you hurting and broken within
Arise my soul
Come and see the King
He who was before there was light
How great the chasm that lay between us
I remember what you did for me
In the darkness we were waiting
King of Heaven, Holy one
Light pierced through the dark
Oh God, how could I stand
Oh the mystery
Sent by the Father, Jesus has come
This Jesus that carried our shame
Your blood is healing ev'ry wound

JUSTICE

Your blood is healing ev'ry wound

LOVE AND DEVOTION

Amazing love! How can it be
Holy Spirit, guide my vision
I love you Lord, oh your mercy never fails me
I'm caught up in your presence
Let this place be an upper room where your
people learn to wait
Oh the mystery
Oh Yahweh, my heart is yours
The more I behold you
There is a throne with rainbow colours blazing
all around
There is no one like you, Jesus son of God
We are the bride and we are waiting
When we least expect it you arrive

MERCY, GRACE AND FORGIVENESS

Amazing love! How can it be
Are you hurting and broken within
Eternal Father, gracious King
For what we have done and left undone
How great the chasm that lay between us
I remember what you did for me
I was lost and searched within
Light in the darkness, beheld the dawn of days
Magnificent, marvelous, matchless love
Mercy every morning, rising like the dawn
Oh God, how could I stand
There is a throne with rainbow colours blazing
all around
There is no one like you, Jesus son of God
This Jesus that carried our shame
When I once was lost
When you appear, our lives are changed
Your love came first

MISSION

Come and see the King
Did you know, did you know
Sent by the Father, Jesus has come
To see the outcast accepted

MYSTERY/TRANSCENDENCE AND POWER OF GOD

Amazing love! How can it be
Come and see the King
Come Holy Spirit, fill us now
He who was before there was light
In the darkness we were waiting
Just one word
Let this place be an upper room where your
people learn to wait
Oh the mystery
Piercing through the dark, you shine your light
There is no one like you, Jesus son of God
When the Word of God was first heard on earth

PRAISE AND THANKSGIVING

Come and see the King
Come let us worship our King
From life's beginning
God, you brought us out of the wilderness
How great the chasm that lay between us
Just one word
King of Heaven, Holy one
Let everything that has breath praise the Lord
Let praise be a weapon
Light in the darkness, beheld the dawn of days
Light pierced through the dark

Oh Yahweh, my heart is yours
There is no one like you, Jesus son of God
We are the bride and we are waiting
Were creation suddenly articulate
Your love came first

PRAYER AND INTERCESSION

Eternal Father, gracious King
Just like you did in days of old
Piercing through the dark, you shine your light
To see the outcast accepted
You are the river that won't run dry

PROCLAMATION

Arise my soul
Come and see the King
I just want to speak the Name of Jesus
I raise a hallelujah
I was lost and searched within
Just one word
Light pierced through the dark
Piercing through the dark, you shine your light
There is a throne with rainbow colours blazing all around
This Jesus that carried our shame
When I once was lost
When you appear, our lives are changed
You are here, moving in our midst
Your blood is healing ev'ry wound

RENEWAL AND REFRESHMENT

Come and see the King
Come Holy Spirit, fill us now
Come like you want to
Fill my lungs with the wind of your Spirit
I'm caught up in your presence
I've found life in the desert
Made in this world but not made of it
Piercing through the dark, you shine your light
The Holy One has just walked in
The Lord is my Shepherd, he goes before me
The more I behold you
This Jesus that carried our shame
When we least expect it you arrive
When you appear, our lives are changed
You are here, moving in our midst

RESPONSE

Always true, always kind
Amazing love! How can it be
Are you hurting and broken within
Eternal Father, gracious King
For what we have done and left undone

He who was before there was light
Here in this moment you are able
Holy Spirit, guide my vision
How great the chasm that lay between us
I love you Lord, oh your mercy never fails me
I raise a hallelujah
Just like you did in days of old
Let this place be an upper room where your people learn to wait
Made in this world but not made of it
Oh Yahweh, my heart is yours
The Holy One has just walked in
To see the outcast accepted
When I once was lost

SPIRITUAL WARFARE

Come Holy Spirit, fill us now
Come let us worship our King
Come like you want to
Here in this moment you are able
I just want to speak the Name of Jesus
I raise a hallelujah
I remember what you did for me
I was lost and searched within
Just one word
Let praise be a weapon
The Lord is my Shepherd, he goes before me
When I once was lost
When you appear, our lives are changed
Your love came first

SUFFERING AND TRIALS

Always true, always kind
Fill my lungs with the wind of your Spirit
I just want to speak the Name of Jesus
I raise a hallelujah
The Lord is my Shepherd, he goes before me
Were creation suddenly articulate
Your love came first

SUITABLE FOR SOLO OR PRESENTATION

I just want to speak the Name of Jesus
The Holy One has just walked in
The more I behold you
When we least expect it you arrive

TRINITY

Eternal Father, gracious King
In the darkness we were waiting
Magnificent, marvelous, matchless love
Sent by the Father, Jesus has come
Your love came first